ASL Concepts Presents

DEAF CULTURE
COLORING BOOK

WRITTEN BY: JESSICA PARKER

Copies may be purchased from
ASL Concepts
1120 Huffman Rd. Suite 24 #771
Anchorage, Alaska 99515
www.aslconcepts.com
aslconceptsak@gmail.com
1-844-667-3524
First printing 2019

Acknowledgements

I would like to express my gratitude to the many people who saw me through this stage of curriculum writing. This book is more than just a coloring book; it represents the next stage of developing curriculum materials for Deaf children after a year of research. In working toward my doctorate in curriculum and instruction, I surveyed hundreds of deaf education teachers and deaf institutes asking for input regarding what specific materials would be most useful for developing ASL literacy in Deaf children. I am grateful to the many who shared their experiences and gave me suggestions on how to best meet the needs of deaf education teachers in the classroom. You can view the entire dissertation study-"Teacher's Preparation to Teach Deaf Students ASL: A Phenomenological Qualitative Investigation of Perceptions, Processes, and Current Practices" online at www.aslconcepts.com.

Since this is a very visual book, representing American Sign Language accurately through images and pictures was an essential piece. Thanks to Camille and Lin who contributed their artistic talents, bringing this book to completion. Thank you to James Patton, Eve Ooten, and Patrick Fischer for your feedback in accurately portraying ASL. Thank you to my network of illustrators, designers, and formatters: Shehryar, Nimrah, Camille, Lin, and Rob. Ginny Patton co-wrote this book and her contributions were invaluable. Thank you to my husband, Jeremy Parker, for his editing skills. And finally, thank you to my intern KatLynn Powell for helping with countless projects, which allowed this book to be finalized. Creating materials such as these takes an entire team of people and I am forever grateful!

ASL CONCEPTS DEAF CULTURE BOOK FAQ's

What is ASL Concepts?

ASL Concepts is a small company based in Anchorage, Alaska focusing on providing excellent American Sign Language curriculum materials, instruction, and advocacy to the field of American Sign Language. We focus on teaching the language alongside grammar, history, and culture. We create meaningful ASL materials including children's stories, ASL workbooks, teacher curriculum guides, coloring books, posters, games, and other supplemental materials.

Who develops the ASL Concepts materials, and do they have authentic signing and Deaf cultural experience?

Jessica Parker is the owner of ASL Concepts. She is a CODA, a Child of a Deaf Adult. The children's book "My Dad is Deaf" is a story written from her own personal experiences growing up with a Deaf father. ASL is her native language. Jessica has extensive ASL teaching experience and ASL curriculum development skills. That being said, the many projects of ASL Concepts require a large team of individuals. All contributors are either Deaf, CODAs, ASL interpreters, or people immersed in the Deaf world.

How did ASL Concepts get started?

Anchorage, Alaska has a remote population of Deaf students, most of whom have limited ASL skills. Jessica Parker was hired to teach ASL classes to Deaf students, developing their native ASL skills. Consequently, their English skills improved. Jessica was discouraged by the lack of ASL curriculum resources for Deaf students and was inspired to do something about it. Most ASL materials are written for hearing students, merely focusing on vocabulary. Deaf educators are modifying ASL curriculum meant for the hearing to suit the needs of the Deaf. Jessica pursued research in developing ASL curriculum for Deaf children, interviewing experienced deaf education teachers, and compiling wish lists from teachers across the nation. Jessica teamed up with a group of native signers and ASL professionals to set up ASL Concepts and create ASL materials for Deaf children.

What is included in the Deaf Culture Coloring Book?

This book features 30 Deaf cultural concepts including: Abraham Lincoln Memorial, ASL Sign, ASL poetry, Chuck Baird, CC Glasses, Closed captioning, CODA, De'VIA, Cochlear implant, Deaf Community, Deaf Culture, Deaf identity, Deaf President Now, Deaflympics, DeafSpace, Eye contact, Flashing doorbell, Football huddle, Gallaudet University, Hard of hearing, Hearing aid, I Love You Sign, Interpreter, Laurent Clerc, Name signs, Sign variations, Thomas Gallaudet, Vibrating alarm, Videophone, and Waving applause. Each concept features a drawing of the Deaf cultural concept, its sign, and explanation about the concept or historical event/person.

What other ASL Concepts materials are available?

There is a Go Fish animal playing card game featuring Alaskan animals and an Alaskan Animal Coloring Book. There are four ASL curriculum books available featuring children's book themes including: Chicka Chicka Boom Boom, Are You My Mother?, Brown Bear, and One Fine Day. There is a chapter book "A World of Knowing" along with a companion study guide, which tells the story of Thomas Gallaudet, the founder of America's first school for the Deaf. ASL Concepts also features two children's books: A Story of ASL and My Dad is Deaf. Check out www.aslconcepts.com for a list of all materials available and coming soon.

What age level are these ASL Concepts materials meant for?

These books were written for Deaf children aged 5-12, approximately kindergarten to 6th grade; however, the information can be tailored to fit any age/grade level, Deaf and hearing. The materials are written for an ASL teacher going into a classroom without having to do extensive preparation. They are ready to go. The goal is to teach ASL using children literature as a bridge between English and ASL, improving both languages. This creates a bilingual education approach, in which the student's language and literacy development are the focus.

Are there ASL Concepts videos?

Yes, all ASL Concept videos are available online for free at www.aslconcepts.com. They are also on YouTube on the deafinthesky channel-https://www.youtube.com/user/deafinthesky. All videos feature native signers. Captioning and voicing are available on all videos.

Can these materials be photocopied for classroom use?

Yes, teachers may purchase one copy and reproduce for classroom use. Materials may not be shared for more than one classroom and care must be taken when used for multiple sources. These original materials were expensive to create. Please do your part to support small businesses such as ASL Concepts who are working relentlessly to create more ASL materials for Deaf children.

Introduction

The Deaf Culture ASL Coloring Book is designed to be used as a fun activity for Deaf or hearing children. It introduces Deaf terminology signs while teaching cultural concepts related to Deaf culture. All of the activities are aligned with National ACTFL (American Council on the Teaching of Foreign Languages), Common Core, and comprehensive K-12 standards for American Sign Language.

How to Guide Young Minds?

- Read the Alaska animal pages together.
- Sign the animals together.
- Have students color the sign and animal.
- Give students praise and encouragement.
- Award students with the Mastery Certificate.

ACTFL and Common Core Standards

Interpersonal-Students can sign the Deaf cultural concepts with their peers.

Interpretive-Students can recognize the Deaf cultural concept signs when signed to them.

Presentational-Students can sign the Deaf cultural concept signs and present the matching images to each sign.

Cultures-Students can learn about Deaf cultural concepts and their relevance to the Deaf community.

CCSS.ELA-LITERACY.RI.2.1-Ask and answer such questions as who, what, where, when, why, and how to demonstrate understanding of key details in a text.

CCSS.ELA-LITERACY.RI.2.3-Describe the connection between a series of historical events, scientific ideas or concepts, or steps in technical procedures in a text.

CCSS.ELA-LITERACY.RI.2.7-Explain how specific images contribute to and clarify a text.

CCSS.ELA-LITERACY.L.2.6-Use words and phrases acquired through conversations, reading and being read to, and responding to texts, including using adjectives and adverbs to describe a subject.

CCSS.ELA-LITERACY.RH.6-8.7-Integrate visual information with other information in print and digital texts.

ASL Content Standards

Informational Text.
Key Ideas & Details:
- Grade K. 1. With prompting and support, ask and answer questions about key details.
- Grade 2. 1. Ask and answer such questions as who, what, where, when, and how to demonstrate understanding of key details in a text.

Craft & Structure.
- Grade 1. 3. Distinguish between information provided by pictures or other illustrations and information provided by the finger-spelled signs and signs in a text.
- Grade 2. 1. Determine the meaning of finger-spelled words, signs, and phrases in a text relevant to a grade level topic or subject area.

Integration of Knowledge & Ideas.
- Grade 2. 1. Explain how specific images contribute to and clarify a text.

Foundational Skills.
- Sign Concepts. Grades K-1. 1. Demonstrate understanding of the organization and basic features of sign.
- Phonological Awareness. Grades K-1. 1. Demonstrate understanding of signs and parameters.
- Morphological Awareness. Grades K-2. 1. Know and apply grade-level sign analysis skills in decoding signs.
- Fluency. Grades K-2. 1. View and sign on-level texts with sufficient accuracy and fluency to support comprehension.

Published Signing.
- Text Types & Purposes. Grades 3-5. 2. Sign informative/explanatory texts to examine a topic and convey ideas and information clearly.
- Discourse & Presentation Standards. Grades K-3. 2. Confirm understanding of storytelling or story signing or information signed through other media by asking and answering questions about key details and requesting clarification if something is not understood.

Discourse & Presentation Standards.
- Comprehension & Collaboration. Grades K. 2. Confirm understanding of storytelling or story signing or information signed through other media by asking and answering questions about key details and requesting clarification if something is not understood.
- Presentation of Knowledge & Ideas. Grades K-3. 2. Add drawings or other visual displays to descriptions as desired to provide additional detail.

Language Standards.
- Vocabulary Acquisition & Use. Grades K-6. 1. Determine or clarify the meaning of unknown and multiple meaning signs, finger-spelled words, and phrases based on grade level viewing and content.

Abraham Lincoln Memorial

Abraham Lincoln Memorial

Abraham Lincoln granted the creation of a Deaf college in Washington, D.C. now known as Gallaudet University. Lincoln believed everyone deserved "a fair chance in the race of life." Sharing his beliefs, many Deaf felt a connection to Lincoln as a supporter of the Deaf community. It is believed that the Lincoln Memorial (1914) shows the President's hands forming the letters "A" and "L" to show appreciation in his support for the Deaf. After all, the artist, Daniel Chester French had a Deaf son and a strong pulse on the views of the Deaf community. In fact, French created the Gallaudet and Alice statue (1889), which is still proudly displayed at Gallaudet University.

ASL Poetry

ASL
POETRY

ASL Poetry

ASL poetry is a form of ASL literature that uses handshape, repetition, and artistic expression in sign language. It uses the hands and the body to sign words and express vivid images, concepts, thoughts, and emotions. It is a visual literary form, full of facial expressions, that has grown from sign language storytelling. ASL poetry uses different signing speeds, subtle pauses, and figurative language like metaphors, personification, and symbolism. Famous ASL poets include Clayton Valli, Patrick Graybill, Douglas Ridloff, and Crom Saunders.

ASL Sign

ASL Sign

ASL, or American Sign Language, is a visual gestural language used by the Deaf in America and many other parts of the world. It is not a universal language. It uses handshapes, palm orientation, location, movement, and facial expressions to communicate information. It has its own rules for grammar and syntax. In the early 1800's, Thomas Hopkins Gallaudet, a hearing minister, met and became friends with a Deaf girl named Alice. He started teaching Alice and was able to teach her a few words. The girl's father, Dr. Cogswell, asked Gallaudet to become involved with starting the first school for the Deaf in America. In 1815, he traveled to Europe to find ways to teach the Deaf. He visited a Deaf school in Britain, but they refused to share their methods. Then Gallaudet traveled to Paris, France where he met Laurent Clerc, a deaf teacher. In 1817, Gallaudet asked Clerc to return with him to the States. The first American school for the Deaf was established in the City of Hartford, Connecticut. This was the birth of ASL in America.

CC Glasses

CC Glasses

Closed Caption glasses are devices that convert the sound of a film into text onto special glasses. Closed Caption glasses were invented by Randy Smith Jr. to allow the Deaf to understand movies. He had a Deaf son and they would test out the glasses by going to the movies together. After finally building glasses that worked, he received a letter from a parent of a Deaf child stating how special and appreciated the glasses were. Closed Caption glasses have given the Deaf community a gift. They can enjoy a movie along with their hearing friends and families.

Chuck Baird

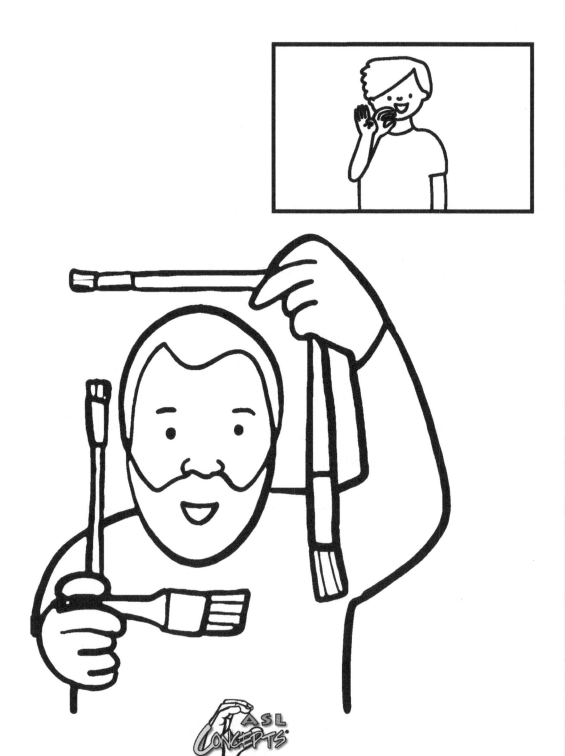

Chuck Baird

Chuck Baird was a famous Deaf artist known as the father of De'VIA/Deaf Art. He was born in Kansas City and graduated from the Kansas School for the Deaf in 1967. He went to Gallaudet University after two years, then attended Rochester Institute of Technology for the Deaf. He, earned a degree in Studio Painting in 1974. He worked at the National Theatre of the Deaf painting sets. His painting talent grew during this time, and he showcased many art shows. He once painted a 150-foot long painting of Deaf history and language for the Learning Center for Deaf Children in Framingham, MA. Chuck Baird was also an actor, teacher, and ASL storyteller. His paintings are about his love of ASL and pride in Deaf culture.

Closed Captioning
TV

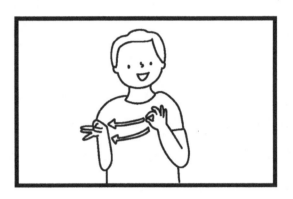

WINDS HAVE PICKED UP AS THE FIRST
MAJOR STORM OF THE SEASON ARRIVES

Closed Captioning
TV

February 15, 1972 was the first time closed captioning was seen. The Deaf could finally turn on their televisions and understand what was being said. More programs for the Deaf started to be captioned including soap operas, talk shows, game shows, sports, and cartoons. In 1982, real-time captioning started, which meant TV shows could be captioned as the event took place. New technologies and methods were developed, such as a caption-decoding microchips, which were built into each new television set. By 1996, digital captioning was required by law on all television programs.

Cochlear Implant

Cochlear Implant

A cochlear implant is a small electronic device that helps people who are Deaf. It is not like a hearing aid, because it is surgically put into the brain. It activates the auditory nerve, which is what we use to hear sounds. Signals are sent to the brain, allowing the Deaf person to hear sounds. These new sounds they hear are different from normal hearing, and it takes time to understand them. Deaf children often receive cochlear implants at a young age, so they can learn language naturally as they grow. Scientists are continuing to improve the technology of cochlear implants. Cochlear implants do not make Deaf people hearing, but they do help them hear language and sounds around them.

Children of Deaf Adults
International

CODA

A CODA is a child of a Deaf adult. Many CODA's know English and American Sign Language. CODA's can fit into both the Deaf and hearing worlds and often serve as a bridge between the two worlds. CODA's often grow up and work in Deaf-related jobs, such as interpreters and ASL teachers. CODA's are a close-knit group because of their shared experiences and love for the Deaf community. There is a CODA organization that holds conferences, CODA camps, and social gatherings. CODA's can be Deaf or hearing, but most often grow up in a Deaf world and exhibit behaviors different from those who can hear.

Community

Community

The Deaf community consists of Deaf, hard of hearing, and hearing people who share the language of ASL. They share similar experiences and have the same way of interacting with each other. Many Deaf say there is a feeling of "home" in the Deaf community. They feel close to each other because of their shared language and an understanding of what it means to be a Deaf person in a hearing world. There are organizations like the NAD, ASLTA, and local Deaf churches that allow the Deaf to come together and express their hearts in ASL. The Deaf community includes many activities that are "Deaf-friendly" such as bowling, coffee chats, and silent dinners. They are a close-knit group that offers a sense of belonging.

Deaf Culture

Deaf Culture

Deaf culture centers revolve around American Sign Language. Deaf culture includes traditions, identity, and values. Values among the Deaf include the importance of clear communication. Deaf clubs are also important, because they offer natural social interaction. Deaf storytelling is highly valued and commonly shared during social events. Typical behaviors within Deaf culture include hug greetings, getting someone's attention by tapping them, using direct eye-contact, and flickering the lights in a room to get everyone's attention. Deaf people are often direct and to the point. Comments that might be thought of as rude to a hearing person are not rude for the Deaf. Deaf culture is important because it allows the Deaf to be who they are without fear of judgement.

Deaflympics

Deaflympics

Deaflympics is a world-wide event where Deaf athletes compete at an elite level. The games have been organized by the International Committee of Sports for the Deaf since the first event in 1924. These games are held every four years. Track races are started by using a light instead of a starter pistol. Football referees use flags, instead of whistles. The games have changed to include the communication needs on the playing field by the Deaf athletes. The spectators do not clap, but instead wave using both hands. Hearing aids and cochlear implants are not allowed in the competition to ensure fairness for all athletes. There are now both summer and winter games, which are held all over the world. The Deaflympics are run and organized by Deaf people for Deaf people.

Deaf President Now

Deaf President Now

Deaf President Now was a protest that happened in 1988 at Gallaudet University, the world's most well-known Deaf university. The university chose a hearing woman to be Gallaudet's next president. The Deaf students were tired of having a hearing leader who did not know ASL or have an understanding of the Deaf community. In reaction to this, Gallaudet students shut down the school and led a protest. The students, staff, and Deaf all over the U.S. showed their support by joining the protest. The protest lasted one week. As a result, the hearing president resigned, and Dr. Irving King Jordan was picked as the first Deaf president of Gallaudet University. The protest changed history, creating positive changes for the Deaf community.

DeafSpace

DeafSpace

DeafSpace is a special building design that includes Deaf people's ideas of living space. DeafSpace's goal is to create spaces that help the Deaf visually and encourage communication. There are five parts included in this design.

- **Sensory**- Windows and walls should be waist-high, so the Deaf can see what is happening in other areas.
- **Space**- The Deaf communicate in ASL, so that means they need a bigger space to be able to sign comfortably.
- **Mobility and proximity**- The Deaf use sign language, so their surroundings need to have clear paths.
- **Light and color**- There should be no glare on windows or busy patterns on walls.
- **Acoustics**- The way sound bounces off walls. The Deaf use hearing aids and cochlear implants, so some sounds are distracting and even painful.

De'VIA

DEAF IDENTITY crayons

1999

Crayon labels: CODA · SEEING · DEAF-BLIND · LATE-DEAFENED · DEAF-AMERICAN · HARD-OF-HEARING · SIGNER · DEAF

ASL CONCEPTS

De'VIA

De'VIA stands for Deaf View/Image Art. It is an art form that shows Deaf experience and culture. Famous De'VIA artists include Betty Miller, Ann Silver, Nancy Rourke, and Chuck Baird. De'VIA has two types of art forms: one is focused on experience, and the other is focused on American Sign Language. One example of De'VIA based on experience is Ann Silver's "Deaf Identity" crayons, which describe labels for the Deaf. An example of De'VIA based on ASL is Chuck Baird's crocodile animal sign painting, which includes the crocodile sign within the picture of a crocodile. De'VIA expresses Deaf emotion and shows the beauty of ASL. This art form is an important part of Deaf culture and a powerful, thriving art form.

Eye Contact

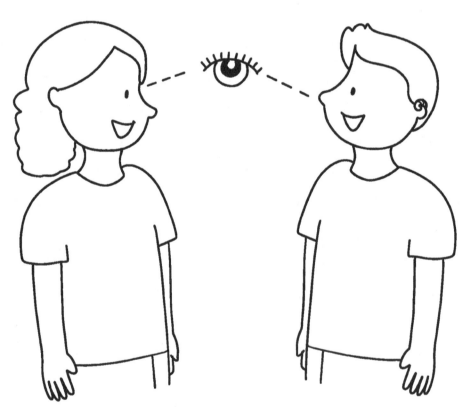

Eye Contact

Eye-contact in the Deaf community is very important! It means you are listening to the conversation. If you break eye-contact, it shows you are no longer listening. This is considered rude and disrespectful. Our eyes communicate attitudes and emotions. The Deaf are looking for feedback through your eyes and depend on this for full understanding. Not keeping eye contact breaks up the conversation and leads to confusion and frustration for the Deaf. This is one of the most important things in Deaf culture, especially because the Deaf use ASL, a visual language to communicate.

Flashing Doorbell

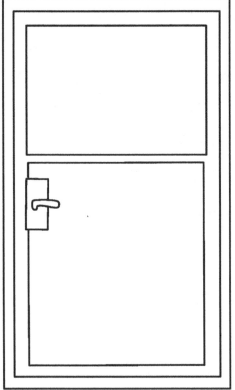

Flashing Doorbell

Flashing doorbells were created to help the Deaf know when they have a visitor at their door. When a person rings a doorbell, a Deaf person cannot hear the sound, so they do not know someone is there. This invention has solved this problem for the Deaf. These doorbells use light to alert them. The doorbell is connected to a light or a system of lights, which flashes throughout the house. This is a wonderful example of how technology has helped the Deaf live more independent lives.

Football Huddle

Football Huddle

In 1892, the Gallaudet football team was playing against another Deaf team. Teams would communicate during their plays by using sign language across the field. Paul Hubbard, the quarterback, didn't want the other team to see him explaining the plays in ASL, so he told them to come around in a close circle to hide his signing. Hearing football teams quickly adopted this strategy, and the football huddle has been used by football teams across America ever since.

Gallaudet University

Gallaudet University

Gallaudet University was founded in 1864 and was named after Thomas Hopkins Gallaudet, the father of American Sign Language. Abraham Lincoln signed the charter for Congress to start the school. It is the first university for education of Deaf and hard of hearing students. Most of Gallaudet University's students as well as many of the teachers are Deaf. They use ASL in all of their classes. Gallaudet University is considered the most famous and respected Deaf school in the world.

Hard of Hearing

Hard of Hearing

Hard of hearing refers to people who have a mild to moderate hearing loss. They might communicate in sign language, spoken language, or both. Their hearing loss may be caused by childhood illness, injury, age, long exposure to loud noises, or infection. A hard of hearing person may be able to hear some sound, but have trouble hearing speech or music. About 5% of the world's population is hard of hearing.

Hearing Aid

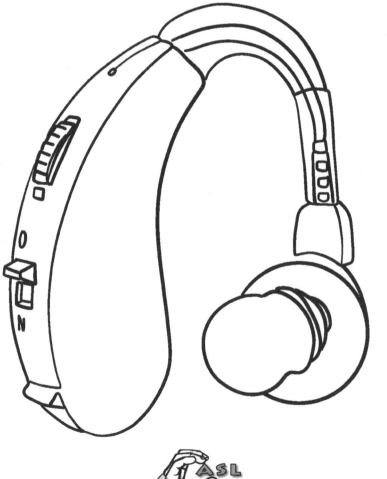

Hearing Aid

A hearing aid is a small electronic device that is worn in or behind the ear. It is worn by Deaf and hard-of-hearing people. A hearing aid improves hearing and speech understanding. Sound is made louder as it enters the ear, allowing hair cells to feel the vibrations and change them into signals in the brain. There are two types of electronics used in hearing aids, analog and digital. Analog hearing aids change sound waves into electrical signals, and digital hearing aids change sound waves into codes, making them louder. Hearing aids are very expensive and often need to be adjusted, especially for children as they grow.

Identity

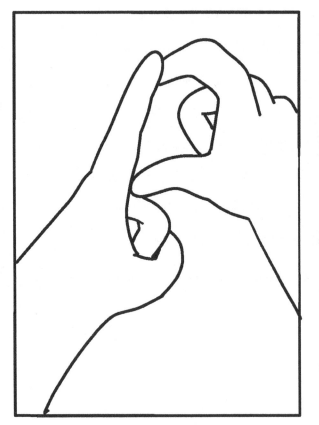

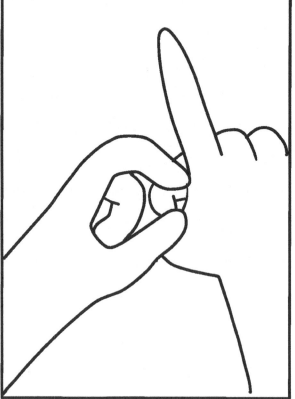

Identity
(BIG D /LITTLE D)

In Deaf culture, there are two different uses of the word "deaf". Using the word Deaf with a capital "D" means a person is a member of the Deaf community and uses American Sign Language. They are involved in Deaf culture and have a strong Deaf identity. They are proud to be Deaf. Using the word "deaf" with a lowercase "d" means they either do not know ASL or are not connected with the Deaf community. They identify themselves more with hearing people. Deaf vs. deaf simply shares the world they connect with the most-the Deaf world or the hearing world and it can say a lot about their identity.

I Love you Sign

I love you Sign

Everywhere you go, you will see people flashing the ILY sign, which is a combination of signing I, L, & Y, meaning "I love you." This sign is understood all over the world, and it is the most recognizable sign in the world. It received media exposure when Richard Dawson used it to sign off his TV show "Family Feud." President Jimmy Carter picked it up and during his inaugural day parade, flashed the ILY to a group of Deaf people watching. The Deaf community uses this sign as a way to say goodbye, similar to a wave. In today's culture, we see creative use of this sign by Spider-Man, Doctor Strange, and the band Kiss. The ILY sign is an expression of positive feelings, from a friendly esteem to genuine love.

Interpreter

Interpreter

An ASL interpreter is a trained person in American Sign Language. Interpreters work in many different places such as schools, hospitals, and community events. They serve as a communication link between the Deaf and the hearing. Interpreters must be skilled at communication and be able to read sign language well. They are professional people who serve the Deaf community and are also language models for young Deaf children who are just learning ASL. There are certain rules for clothing if you are a sign language interpreter. The reason for this is because Deaf people read sign language with their eyes. Having a solid contrasting color lessens eye strain. Interpreters serve a vital function within the Deaf community.

Laurent Clerc

Laurent Clerc

Laurent Clerc was America's first Deaf teacher. When he was one-year old, he fell off a stool into the kitchen fireplace. This caused him to lose his sense of smell and hearing. His name sign is an H handshape, outlining the scar on the side of his face. Laurent was born in 1785 and is famous for his work in deaf education. He grew up in France and was a teacher at a famous Deaf school in Paris. He met Thomas Gallaudet in France and decided to go to America to help establish America's first school for the Deaf in Hartford, Connecticut. Laurent was the head teacher and Gallaudet was the principal of the new school for the Deaf. Laurent was the most influential person in Deaf education history.

Name Signs

Name Signs

Name signs are an important part of Deaf culture. These name signs show the person's characteristics and are usually made using the first initial of the person's name. There are two types of name signs. The first type is arbitrary, which means they do not show the person's appearance or personality. If your name is Thomas, your name sign might be a "T" on your left shoulder. The second kind of name sign is descriptive. These show the person's personality or appearance. For example, if your name is Linda and you have long hair, your name sign might be an "L" that slides down the length of your hair. The Deaf community gives out name signs, and it is considered an honor to receive one. Not all names have signs. Short names such as Tom, Sue, and Bob are just finger-spelled. Name signs are a valued part of Deaf culture.

Sign Variations

Sign Variations

Sign variations are different ways of signing the same word. There are many reasons for sign variations. Regional variations are signs that look different from place to place. For example, the sign for "pizza" in Texas is a bent V hand shape in a zig-zag motion. In Alaska, "pizza" is signed with a curved flat hand shape directed towards the mouth. There are also differences in ASL depending on which community you live in. Black communities often sign differently than white communities; older Deaf sign differently than younger Deaf. They have different slang words and cultural meanings, just like the English word "soda" can be "pop," "coke," or "soft drink." There are different accents in spoken language, so there are different accents in sign language.

Thomas Gallaudet

Thomas Gallaudet

Thomas Gallaudet was an American educator. He, along with Laurent Clerc, founded the first school for the Deaf. In 1814, he was in Hartford, Connecticut where he met a little Deaf girl named Alice Cogswell. Thomas did not know sign language, but he tried to talk to her by pointing to objects and writing words in the dirt. She understood him, and he was excited to teach her to read and write. He didn't know exactly how to teach her, so he traveled to England to visit the Braidwood School for the Deaf, but they refused to share their teaching methods. Gallaudet visited a Deaf school in France. While he was there, he met Laurent Clerc and asked Clerc to go back to America with him. Clerc taught Gallaudet French sign language and Gallaudet taught Clerc English. Together, they established the first American School for the Deaf.

Vibrating Alarm

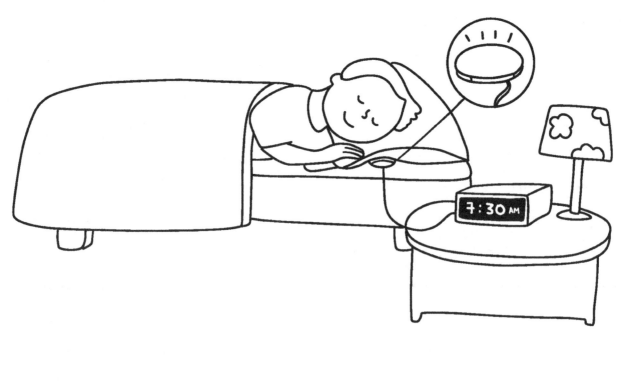

Vibrating Alarm

Living with hearing loss means you need to make some changes in your everyday life. Deaf people cannot hear the buzz of an alarm clock, even if it is set on the loudest sound level. Vibrating alarm clocks are very helpful. These alarm clocks use vibrations that gently shake the pillow. The Deaf can feel these vibrations and are able to wake up easily. These alarm clocks are small and are often placed inside a pillow case on the underside of the pillow with a clip that helps keep the clock in place. The only bad thing is there is no snooze button!

Videophone

Videophone

A videophone is a special device that helps the Deaf communicate with other people. The Deaf can use a videophone to communicate directly with another person, or they can use a sign language interpreter. In the United States, there is a Video Relay Service. VRS has interpreters, so Deaf can make phone calls to hearing people. The video phone is commonly called a VP. This invention has helped the Deaf become independent and connect with other family members.

Waving Applause

Waving Applause

When the Deaf community claps, they twist their hands in the air to visually show applause. This practice of visual applause came from France in 1985. Gerald "Bunny" Burstein told the story of attending the 200th birthday celebration for Laurent Clerc in France. After each speaker was finished, he observed clapping was made by twisting the arms and hands above the head. This stuck with him, and when he returned to America, he shared what he had witnessed in France. The Deaf picked up the French Deaf applause and it spread through American Deaf Culture. This type of applause became especially important during the 1988 Gallaudet "Deaf President Now" protest. Now it is used universally as a way to clap visually within the Deaf community.

References

ASL Content Standards: Kindergarten - Grade 12 [Pdf]. (2018). Washington D.C.: Gallaudet University, Laurent Clerc National Deaf Education Center, and California School for the Deaf-Riverside. https://www.gallaudet.edu/Documents/ASL-Standards/k-12-ASL-Content-Standard.pdf

Bahan, B. (2007). "Face-to Face Tradition in the American DeafCommunity: Dynamics of the Teller, The Tale, and the Audience." In H. Bauman, J. Nelson, H. Rose, & W. Mitchell (Authors), Signing the body poetic: Essays on American sign language literature. Berkley, CA: University of California Press.

Bauman, H. (n.d.). DeafSpace. Retrieved from https://www.gallaudet.edu/campus-design-and-planning/deafspace

Benedict, B., & Legg, J. (n.d.). Deaf Culture & Community. Retrieved from https://www.handsandvoices.org/comcon/articles/deafculture.htm

Berke, J. (2018). How You Receive a Name Sign Within the Deaf Community. Retrieved from https://www.verywellhealth.com/using-name-signs-for-personal-names-1048725

Center, L. & Gallaudet University. (n.d.). Retrieved from https://www3.gallaudet.edu/clerc-center/info-to-go/deaf-culture/american-deaf-culture.html

Baird, Chuck (n.d.). Retrieved from http://www.deafart.org/Biographies/Chuck_Baird/chuck_baird.html

CODA (Children of Deaf Adults, Inc.) strives to achieve our mission via conferences, retreats, publications, scholarships, resource development, and fundraising to enrich the experience of Codas. (n.d.). Retrieved from https://www.codainternational.org/

Dawn Sign Press. (2016). History of American Sign Language. Retrieved from https://www.dawnsign.com/news-detail/historyof-american-sign-language

Deaf Friendly Applause! (2015). Retrieved from https://signlanguageco.com/deaf-friendly-applause/

Deaflympics.com. (n.d.). Retrieved from https://www.deaflympics.com/games

Enders, K. (n.d.). Gallaudet, Thomas Hopkins. Retrieved from https://www.learningtogive.org/resources/gallaudet-thomas-hopkins

H-Direkson, L., Bauman, J., Nelson, L., and Rose, H. Berkely: University of California Press, 2006. 21-50. Pring.

Lane, H., Hoffmeister, R., & Bahan, B. (1996). A Journey into the Deaf-World. San Diego, CA: Dawn Sign Press.

NIDCD. (2017). Cochlear Implants. Retrieved from https://www.nidcd.nih.gov/health/cochlear-implants

Okrent, A. (2014). The True Origin Story of the Football Huddle. Retrieved from https://theweek.com/articles/451763/true-originstory-football-huddle

Padden, C. , & Humphries, T. (2006). Inside Deaf Culture. Cambridge, MA: Harvard University Press.

Perry, D. (2018). How 'Deaf President Now' Changed America. Retrieved from https://psmag.com/education/how-deafpresident-now-changed-america

Rood, R. (2013). New Closed-Captioning Glasses Help Deaf Go out to the Movies. Retrieved from https://www.npr.org/sections/alltechconsidered/2013/05/12/183218751/tnew-closed-captioning-glasseshelp-deaf-go-out-to-the-movies

Vaijayanti, P. (2019). Laurent Clerc Biography. Retrieved from http://victorian-era.org/laurent-clerc.html

World Health Organization. (2019). Deafness and hearing loss. Retrieved from https://www.who.int/news-room/fact-sheets/detail/deafness-and-hearing-loss

ASL Concepts

COMPLETION CERTIFICATE

This certificate is presented to

_____

This certificate is awarded
for having successfully completing the
Deaf Culture Coloring Book

Congratulations on a job well done!

_____

Jessica Parker, Author

Jessica Parker, founder of ASL Concepts, has 20+ years of ASL teaching experience. She holds a Bachelor's and Master's Degree from Dallas Baptist University and is nearing completion of her Ed.D in Curriculum and Instruction. She serves as an executive board member of the ASL Honor Society as the Competitions Coordinator. She teaches ASL in Anchorage, Alaska to deaf and hearing students and has first-hand exposure within the Deaf community as a CODA (Child of a Deaf Adult). With a passion for teaching and writing ASL curriculum, Jessica aims to develop ASL curriculum and materials for schools throughout the nation.

Ginny Patton, Author

Ginny Patton was born in Chicago, Illinois. Growing up with deaf neighbors, she developed a love for the Deaf and their culture- watching their hands move in the air, filling the atmosphere with expression, and beautiful unheard meaning. Her interest and desire to be involved in this culture grew along with her. She has served as an ASL interpreter for 35 years. She is married to her husband, James, who is a Deaf pastor. Together they have a Deaf church in Anchorage, Alaska called Hands of Faith. She has six children and five beautiful grandchildren. She works alongside her daughter, Jessica Parker, in creating various ASL tools and curriculum. Fostering an appreciation for ASL and Deaf culture is a constant source of joy in her life.

ASL Concepts aims to provide excellent curriculum materials, instruction, and advocacy to the field of American Sign Language. Deaf culture is woven into every element of the curriculum. You can find more information about ASL Concepts at www.aslconcepts.com

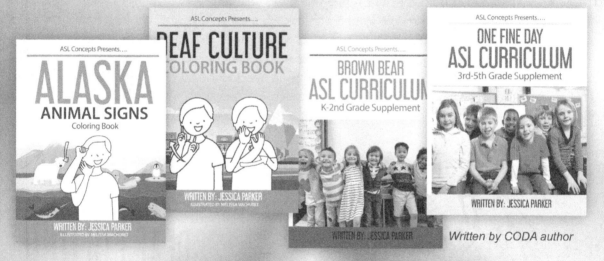

Made in the USA
Coppell, TX
05 August 2022

80990270R00044